The EFT Palace of Possibilities

Presents

Tapping For Kids

By Angie Muccillo

Illustrations by
Sheryl Tongue

The EFT Palace of Possibilities Presents
Tapping For Kids

ISBN 1873483 503
First Edition, First Printing

Published by
DragonRising Publishing
18 Marlow Avenue
Eastbourne
East Sussex BN22 8SJ
United Kingdom
www.DragonRising.com

Printed and bound by CPI Antony Rowe, Eastbourne

Illustrations by Sheryl Tongue
who thanks Jakobi for his untiring patience in posing
for the TapMeister.

Tapping For Kids

Dedication

Tapping For Kids is dedicated to
my amazing nephew Rohan
and all the Children Of The World
in Love and Hope.

WITH GRATITUDE TO:

Gary Craig for creating and sharing EFT
and providing Humanity with a special tool
and vision for achieving peace and freedom.

Dr. Silvia Hartmann for her inspiration,
guidance, support, expertise and wisdom in
helping to make my EFT children's book
a reality.

Angie Muccillo

Contents

Introduction

This is a story about the learning adventures of a group of kids, aged 7 to 11, who visit the world famous EFT Palace of Possibilities. The Palace is a purpose-built, multilevel, learning high-rise, where kids go to learn the tips, tricks and tools of the EFT tapping trade—a popular new kids movement taking the world by storm!

The Tapping Trend

The tapping trade is a new and growing trend with many kids these days. Every day more and more kids like you are discovering they have the built-in ability to change how they feel, anytime they want, simply by mastering the art of tapping—a most handy skill that no kid should be without!

Meet the TapMeister

Palace Guide and Caretaker, Meister Tapper, whom all the children call TapMeister, has been teaching kids how to

tap for over five years now. TapMeister is well known in EFT circles for his skill and dedication in teaching kids how to turn upset feelings into joy, calm and happiness. TapMeister is very excited about sharing with you all the tips, tricks and tools of the tapping trade!

Tapping for Kids

TapMeister teaches that the trick to feeling happy and calm is to tap anytime you feel hurt, lonely, sad or angry. At the Palace of Possibilities you will learn that by tapping *Magic Happy Buttons* on your body using the *Magic Wands* at your fingertips, all the upset inside just vanishes and you can get on with playing, having **fun**, and feeling happy, peaceful and calm again. Just what being a kid is all about, yes?

Finger Tapping Fun!

Finger Tapping Fun! is the official Palace Theme Song. It's quite catchy, so you might find yourself clapping or tapping along to it. Here's how it goes:

Rap-a-tap tapping
With my fingers,
Rap-a-tap tapping
On my face,
Rap-a-tap tapping
Is energizing!
And helps me find
My happy place!

Rap-a-tap tapping
With my fingers,
Rap-a-tap tapping
On my face,
Rap-a-tap tapping
Calms me down
And helps me find
My peaceful space!

Would YOU like to master the art of tapping? Are you ready to join the tapping trend?

Join TapMeister and you too can become part of this popular kid's movement towards peace and calm. TapMeister has plenty of surprises for YOU!

CHAPTER 1

Welcome to TapMeister's Palace of Possibilities For Kids!

• • •

"Welcome girls and boys
to the **Palace of Possibilities**."

• • •

With a warm, glowing smile, TapMeister swings open the door of the **Palace of Possibilities** and ushers in all the kids who are arriving in anticipation of today's EFT tapping lesson.

• • •

"It is with great pleasure that I welcome all of you
to this very fine **Palace**. Since opening it's doors
12 months ago, the **Palace** has been a true hub of
energy and excitement for thousands of kids, all
keen to be part of the tapping trend. I am most

delighted to have you here today to share with you
all that the **Palace of Possibilities** has to offer."

"Come on! Let's see what this tapping trade
is all about shall we?"

• • •

Tapping for Kids Playshop

All the kids here today have signed up for TapMeister's **Tap-ping For Kids Playshop**, an exciting new program where kids learn how to tap into their inner "magic" powers to experience more fun and happiness. In this **Playshop**, TapMeister will lead the kids on a fascinating journey as he explains exactly how EFT works, as well as how to do EFT and when to use it! By the end of today's **Playshop**, the kids will have learnt all the basics of how to tap away their inner troubles using the magic of EFT!

Imagine being able to go from sad to happy, angry to calm, worried to relaxed, all at the press of a "magic button" or two! The kids can hardly wait to awaken their inner magical powers!

A Palace Orientation Tour

TapMeister waits until all the children have sat down and are listening and then he begins to explain what they are going to learn. In his hand he holds a scroll of paper.

• • •

"Before we start on our journey let me tell you a
little bit about the different rooms inside the **Palace**.
These are specially designed rooms, boys and girls,
for learning the tips, tricks and tools of the tapping
trade. Each room has its own unique purpose and fun
lesson to help you learn the art of tapping.

"On this scroll of paper is a map of the **Palace**
with the name of each room and what floor it is on.
There are 8 floors, all of which are easily accessible

from the elevator. The **Palace Elevator** will be our means of transport to the upper floors.

"The ground floor is known as **The Energy Room** where you will learn all about how your body's energy system works.

"The first floor contains **The Activation Room** where you will activate your inner powers by learning where to locate your *Magic Happy Buttons*.

"The second floor is home to **The Dial-Up Room** where you will learn to make a special dial called a **Feel-O-Meter** to help you call up your feelings.

"The third floor houses **The Anger Workout Room**, where you will learn how to 'work out' your anger.

"The fourth floor houses **The Worry Workout Room**, where you will learn how to 'work out' your worries.

"The fifth floor is home to **The Sadness Workout Room**, where you will learn how to 'work out' your sadness.

"The sixth floor is home to **The Esteem-Generator Room**, where you will learn to become your own Esteem Generator.

"The seventh floor contains **The Practice Room**, where you will learn how to practice using your inner powers everyday.

"The eighth floor is on the Top Floor which is home to **The Graduation Room**, where you will get your certificate for participating in the **Playshop**.

"Our first stop today will be **The Energy Room**. It is the foundation upon which the **Palace** is built and therefore it is on the ground floor of this **Palace High-Rise**. It is on the ground floor that we must first enter to make sure you get all the basics before moving up to the next floor.

"So let's go into **The Energy Room** and begin our lessons for today!"

• • •

CHAPTER 2

The Energy Room
Ground Floor

The kids settle into **The Energy Room** on the ground floor where they are about to learn their first lesson in energy.

First Lesson of the Day: The Body's Energy System

• • •

"Well kids, let's begin with our first lesson of the day—*The Body's Energy System.*

"First of all boys and girls, did you know that there is an *Energy System* within each and every one of us? The only trouble is…it's invisible! A problem you may think? Not So! Even though we can't see it, we CAN FEEL IT!

"So the first thing we are going to do is to learn how to FEEL our own energy."

• • •

Building An Energy Ball

• • •

"Okay boys and girls—are you ready to build
an *Energy Ball*?"

• • •

"Yeeessss!" call out the kids excited and curious at the same time.

• • •

"I will show you how, let's begin.

"I want everyone to stand up. Begin by rubbing
your hands together very fast as though you are
trying to warm your hands on a cold day until they
feel toasty."

• • •

The kids rub their hands together as fast as they can until they are nearly a blur.

• • •

"Now hold your hands in front of you with
your palms facing each other and your fingers
slightly curled."

• • •

As TapMeister demonstrates, the kids move their hands into position.

• • •

"Next, move your hands away from each other and
then move them back again, very slowly, in and out,
and keep doing this over and over again."

• • •

The kids move their hands in and out as TapMeister demonstrates this move.

• • •

"Can anyone feel a ball of energy
building up between their hands?"

• • •

"Yes I can feel it; it's weird," calls out Dylan.

"I can feel this funny pressure between my hands," calls out Rohan, amazed at what it feels like.

"That's cool!" yells out Oliver, "I can feel it too!"

"Wow, that's amazing," says Sophie. "I can actually feel my hands tingling."

"I can't see it, but I can feel it!" says Hannah

• • •

"You have just felt your body's energy! This is energy, YOUR energy and it is your *Internal Energy System.*

"The energy in your body is just like electricity. It runs through you all the time, powering your body. We can't see electricity either, can we, but we know it's there. Just like electricity travels through a circuitry of electrical wires, the energy in our bodies travels through imaginary lines that the Chinese people call Meridians. Chinese doctors have a name for this invisible energy—it's called 'Chi.' Just like a car needs petrol to keep the motor going, the body needs Chi energy to keep it running smoothly."

• • •

Energy and Emotions

• • •

"If you look at the word emotion, girls and boys, you will notice that an e-motion is actually just 'energy in motion.' The 'E' stands for 'energy' and 'motion' stands for movement.

"When you are scared or angry or sad, for example, the energy in your body gets stuck or freezes up and can't move. This can form a block or a disruption in the body's energy flow.

7

"When you feel happy and peaceful, on the other hand, the energy in your body is able to move freely without any interruptions, blocks or disruptions.

"The good news is that tapping can release this blocked or stuck energy to get it moving again. When energy is moving again, your emotions change and you instantly feel better.

"Here's a rhyme to help you understand how energy and emotions work."

• • •

I Am a Ball of Energy

In me and through me, energy flows.
Where does it come from? Where does it go?
Like electricity, it courses through me.
Now I know I'm a ball of energy!

From the top of my head to the tips of my toes,
Invisible Chi flows and flows.
In rivers and circuits throughout my body
Sometimes I think I can feel the energy!

The funny thing is…this invisible energy,
It flows more smoothly when I'm feeling happy.
Just like water running down a stream,
When energy flows, life is but a dream!

But when I'm feeling upset, down and out
Or very sad and full of doubt,
It's like an electrical zzzzt
Blocks the energy out!

Like a short circuit in a television set,
When I'm unhappy, my energy goes zzzzztt!
The unhappy emotion, it gets trapped.
But to release it all I do is TAP TAP TAP!

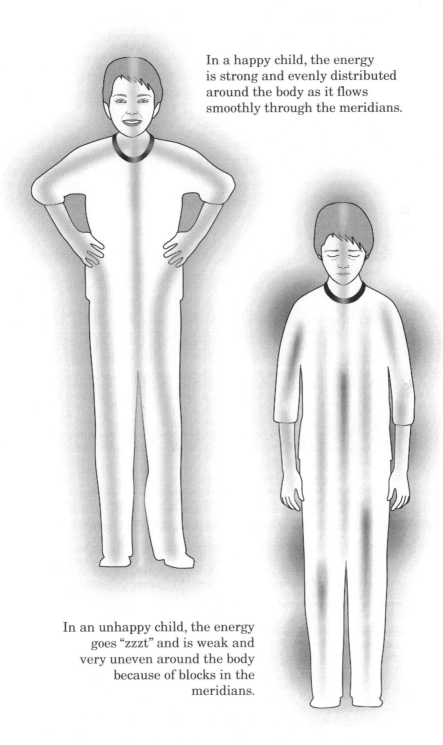

In a happy child, the energy is strong and evenly distributed around the body as it flows smoothly through the meridians.

In an unhappy child, the energy goes "zzzt" and is weak and very uneven around the body because of blocks in the meridians.

• • •

"So boys and girls, as you can see, we tap on our bodies to unblock stuck energy. If we are upset, it means that energy is stuck, disrupted, or caught up somewhere and cannot flow smoothly along the meridians. By tapping we can smooth out the flow of energy. So, who can tell me what happens when energy is flowing?"

• • •

"We feel happy and calm!" calls out Sam.

• • •

"Yes, well done Sam, that's right. Does everyone understand now how energy works?"

• • •

"Yeeess, TapMeister" call out the kids, excited by their new discovery.

• • •

"Excellent…now that we understand the basics of energy, we can move on to our next lesson where we learn about our *Magic Happy Buttons*. Let's get into the elevator and travel up to the first floor to **The Activation Room** where we will learn how to activate our *Magic Wands* for tapping our *Magic Happy Buttons*!"

• • •

CHAPTER 3

The Activation Room
First Floor

Once the kids are settled into **The Activation Room**, TapMeister begins with the second lesson of the day.

**Second Lesson of the Day: Magic Wands
& Happy Button Activations**

• • •

"Well kids, let's continue with our second lesson. I will show you how to activate your *Magic Happy Buttons* using the *Magic Wands* located right at your fingertips!

"*Magic Happy Buttons*, boys and girls, are special spots on your body that you can tap on with your fingertips. The trick is to learn how to unblock

these spots so energy can flow through them and we can feel peace and calm. *Magic Happy Buttons* can be used any time you want to turn unhappy emotions and feelings into happy ones! That's where our *Magic Wands* come in veerrry handy!

"Are we ready to activate our *Magic Wands*, boys and girls?"
• • •

"Yeeeess TapMeister!" call out the kids, ready and excited about switching on their wands.

• • •
"Hold out your hands in front of you and wiggle your fingers like this. Now imagine each and every one of your fingers has turned into a magic wand. Simply say these magic words after me while you wiggle your fingers, to activate your *Magic Wands*."

I am, I am, I am a magic wand
I am, I am, I am switched ON.
I can now wave my wands whenever I please
And turn my troubles into ease!!

"Your *Magic Wands* have now been activated! That means they have been switched on and are ready for use! Now let's find out where our *Magic Happy Buttons* are, shall we?

"Please join me in doing the *Happy Button Rap*. This will help you learn and remember how to find those happy buttons."
• • •

The Happy Button Rap!

Happy buttons are easy to find
Once I learned how
I can use them anytime!

The first spot to remember is
The Karate Chop.
Tapping the sides of my hands,
I just let one drop!

On the top of my head is
The Chimney Top.
I can let off steam
When I tap on this spot!

On to **The High Brow**
between my eyebrows
Near the centre of my face,
I get it now...

Next is **The Sigh Brow**,
to the side of the eye.
Where my brow ends,
I can let out a sigh!

It's time for **The Low Brow**
just below my eye.
When I tap on this spot
I feel a little high!

Under my nose and
above my lip.
It's an easy spot to tap.
Can you feel the dip?

*Now onto my chin
and below my lip.
When I tap this spot,
I start to grin!*

The Tarzan Thump *at the
centre of my chest.
I can pound this spot
To feel my best!*

*When I slap with my palms
under each of my arms,
Do I look like a monkey?
Who cares, I feel calm!*

• • •

"There you have it, kids. You now know where your
happy buttons are! Usually we tap on each spot
about five times to really get that energy moving!
We just did *one round of tapping*. Practice tapping
on them for a while until you get the hang of it."

• • •

The TapMeister watches as the kids practice tapping on their
happy buttons, impressed with the energy and enthusiasm in the
room!

• • •

"A little tip here. Whenever you finish tapping
make sure you remember to take a long deep
breath in and out, filling up your belly until
you see it expand! This also helps to get
your energy moving!

"Okay girls and boys, next you will learn another
important trick of the tapping trade and that is
how to measure your feelings. Into the elevator and
up to the next floor we go!"

• • •

The Dial-Up Room
Second Floor

Once the kids are settled into **The Dial-Up Room**, Tap-Meister begins with the third lesson of the day.

Third Lesson of The Day: Making a Feel-O-Meter

• • •

"Our next lesson today begins with making a 'Feel-O-Meter.' This is a very important tool in mastering the tapping trade!

"A **Feel-O-Meter** is like a thermometer that shows your temperature in feelings. It is a special dial to help you call up your feelings.

"Are you ready to make your very own personal **Feel-O-Meter?**"

• • •

"Yeeeesss TapMeister!" call out the kids, eager to start.

TapMeister hands out a piece of card that is the shape of a semicircle. The semicircle is divided up into 10 sections and has a pointer on it that is able to swing through each of the sections. It looks a bit like half a clock face with only one hand on it.

A Feel-O-Meter

• • •

"Okay boys and girls, this is a **Feel-O-Meter**. One side of the dial will represent your 'good/happy' feelings and the other side of the dial will represent your 'bad/unhappy' feelings. So, on one side of the semicircle I want you to write a word or draw a picture that shows you feeling GREAT! On the other side of the dial I want you to write a word or draw a picture that shows you feeling really BAD!

"With your colored pens, I now want you to color in each section of your dial using whatever colors

you choose. Start with the color you would use for
feeling great and use a different color in
each section until you get to the last section for
feeling bad."

• • •

Once the kids have all finished coloring in their dials, Tap-Meister has a look around to see what everyone has created.

• • •

"Would anyone like to hold up their card?"

• • •

"Me, Me," calls out Angus. His **Feel-O-Meter** has 'Cool' at
one side of the scale and 'Aaaaaaaaaargh!' at the other side.

• • •

"Excellent Angus!

"Now that we have made our very own personal
Feel-O-Meter, let's practice using them by moving
into the first of our **Workout Rooms** where you
will get to 'Exercise' your *Magic Wands* to change
unhappy feelings and emotions into happy ones!

"Into the elevator and up to the next floor we go"

• • •

CHAPTER 5

The Anger Workout Room
Third Floor

First Exercise of The Day: An Anger Workout

• • •

"Our first 'Workout' is an exercise in releasing
angry energy. In the tapping trade, a very
important trick is to 'tune in' to a problem. That
means thinking about the problem. You can also
play a movie of it in your mind. So before we tap,
it's important to choose a problem that is upsetting
you. Do you sometimes get angry, boys and girls?"

• • •

"Yeeeesss, TapMeister" everyone calls out, nodding their
heads in agreement.

Tuning In To Anger

• • •

"The first thing I want you to do is think of
something that is making you angry right now."

• • •

"I'm angry because my friend won't give back my game. She just ignores me when I ask her," says Sophie.

"I'm angry with my mum because she won't let me have a party for my birthday," says Phoebe.

"I'm angry because my dad says I can't have a dog," says Dylan.

"I get really mad when other kids call me names and make fun of me," says Angus.

"I'm mad because no one listens to me," says Antonia.

"I'm really mad at my little brother for biting me all the time," says Oliver.

"I'm angry because my big sister treats me like I don't know anything!" says Jemima.

• • •

"Next I want you to show me what you do or feel
like doing when you get angry."

• • •

"I blow my stack. I feel like fuming!" says Oliver.

"I grit my teeth!" calls out Sophie.

"I stomp my feet!" calls out Angus.

"I screw up my face!" calls out Rohan.

"I run and hide!" calls out Dylan.

"I scream and yell!" calls out Phoebe.

"I cry to mum!" calls out Sam.

"I want to throw something!" calls out Jemima.

• • •

"Thank you everyone!
Being angry doesn't sound like much fun, huh?"

• • •

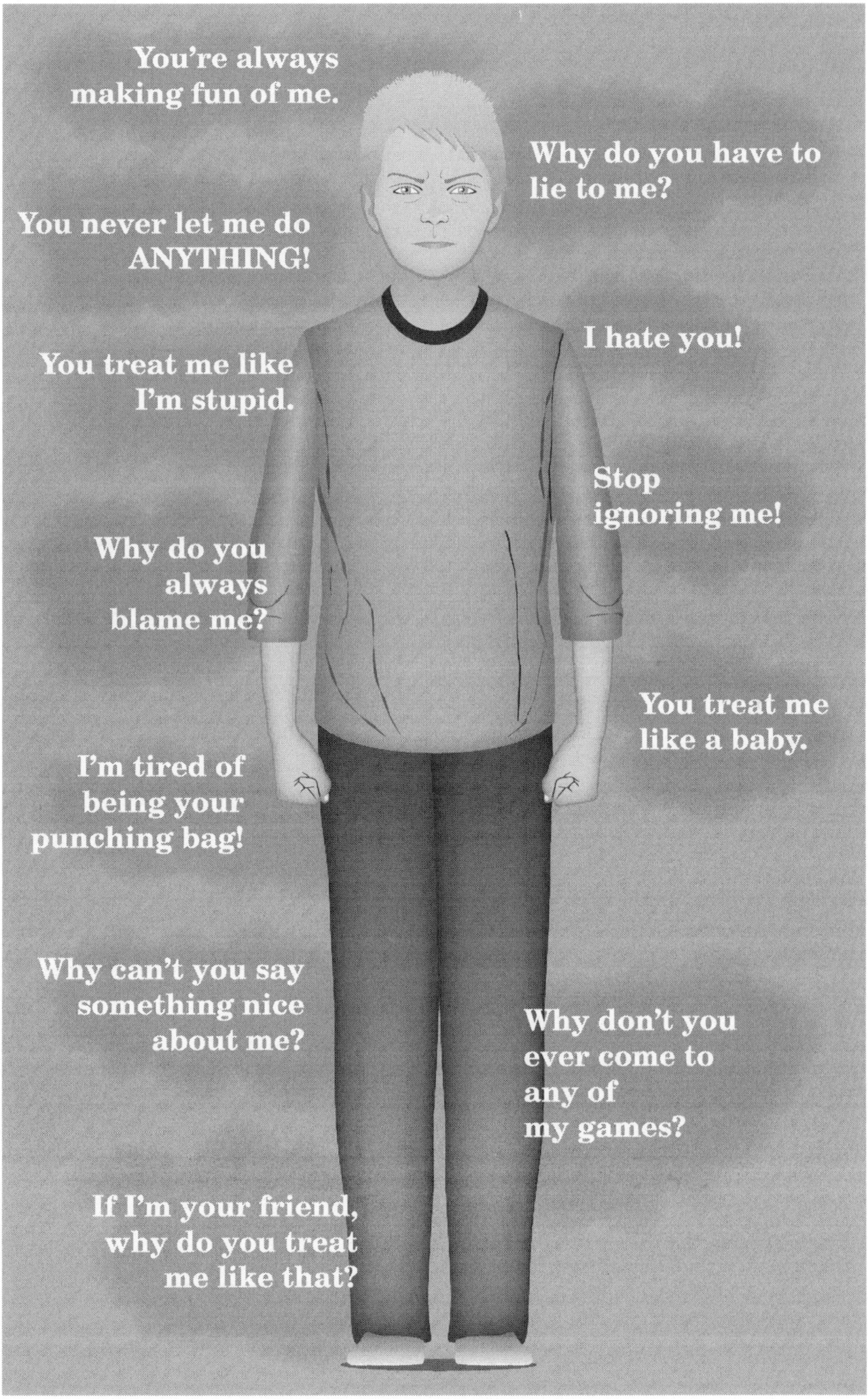
You're always making fun of me.
Why do you have to lie to me?
You never let me do ANYTHING!
I hate you!
You treat me like I'm stupid.
Stop ignoring me!
Why do you always blame me?
You treat me like a baby.
I'm tired of being your punching bag!
Why can't you say something nice about me?
Why don't you ever come to any of my games?
If I'm your friend, why do you treat me like that?

Getting An Anger Rating

• • •

"Once you are tuned in to that angry feeling, I want you to pick up your **Feel-O-Meter**. Now with your pointer, I want you to move it to the section on your dial that shows how angry you are about this right now."

• • •

The kids all move their pointers to a section on their dial.

• • •

"Excellent, we all now have an *Anger* rating on our dials.

"Remember that when you think about something that makes you angry, your energy automatically gets disrupted. Now that we have called up a disruption by thinking about our anger, let's blast it free with EFT!"

• • •

The Anger Workout Tapping Script
The Set Up

• • •

"The first part of tapping is called a '*Set Up*.' In the tapping trade, a *Set Up* is used to help us 'tune in' to the problem.

"To do the *Set Up* we tap on our karate chop with the side of our hand while we say a *Set Up* sentence three times. To learn how to do this I want you to 'tune in' to your angry thoughts and feelings and repeat this set up sentence after me:"

Even though I'm reeeeeeeealy mad,
I'm still a great kid and I set this anger free.

Even though I'm sooooooooo mad,
I'm still a great kid and I set this anger free.

Even though I have all this anger inside,
I'm still a great kid and set this anger free.

"Once we have finished the *Set Up* sentence, we start tapping on our **Magic Happy Buttons** while listing all the things we do when we get angry.

"Now tapping on **The Chimney Top** at the top of your head say out aloud:"

I'm soooo mad I could blow my stack!

"Tap on **The High Brow** just between your eyebrows and while stomping your feet say out aloud:"

I could stomp my feet, I'm so maaaad!

"Tap on **The Sigh Brow** to the side of your eye and through gritted teeth, say out aloud:"

I'm sooo mad I could grit my teeth!

"Tap on **The Low Brow** just below your eye and while screwing up your face, say out aloud:"

I'm sooo mad I could screw up my face!

"Tap **under your nose** and say out aloud:"

I'm sooo mad I could scream and yell!

"Tap **on your chin**, under your lip and say out aloud:"

I'm sooo mad I could run and hide and cry and cry!

"Tap **under your arms** by slapping them with your palms and say out aloud:"

I'm sooo mad I could throw something.

"Tap on **The Tarzan Thump** on your chest
and say out aloud:"

But I'm still a great kid and I set this anger free!
I am happy and calm.
I am happy and calm and relaxed now.
I am peaceful and happy and calm.

"Now, take a long deep breath in and out, filling
up your belly until you see it expand! Well done
everyone! That was quite an anger workout huh?"

• • •

Getting A Post-Tapping Anger Rating

• • •

"Now back to your **Feel-O-Meter** so we can check the
temperature of our feelings again. What I want you to
do is think again about what was making you angry
before we started tapping. Now, with your pointer, I
want you to move it to the section on your dial that
shows how angry you are about that right now."

• • •

All the kids adjust their dials. It seems everyone's anger went
all the way down!

"I feel really COOL now, TapMeister," calls out Rohan.

"I can't remember what I was angry about anymore," calls out
Sam, looking rather puzzled.

"Hey, the anger just melted away!" says Antonia.

"That's funny. It's gone. I can't get angry about it anymore!"
says Angus.

"I feel much better now," calls out Caitlin, with a beaming
smile.

"Hey! This tapping stuff really works!" says Sam.

"I was really mad at my brother for biting me, but I don't care
anymore. He's only little; he doesn't mean it," says Oliver.

"TapMeister, I'm not as angry as before, but I'm still a bit angry, what shall I do?" asks Phoebe.

Second Round of Tapping

• • •

"Phoebe, that brings me to another important trick
of the tapping trade. If, after one round of tapping,
you still feel some of the anger or upset feeling,
just do another round of tapping. Before you do,
remember to 'tune in' to what is still making you
angry so that you can tap it free.

"Tapping on your **Karate Chop**, repeat this 'set up'
after me,"

*Even though I'm still a bit angry,
I'm a great kid and I set the rest of this anger free.*

*Even though I still feel angry,
It's okay and I set the rest of this anger free.*

*Even though a part of me might want to stay angry,
I'm still a great kid and I set the rest of this anger free.*

"Now tapping on **The Chimney Top** at the top of
your head say out aloud:"

I'm still a bit angry.

"Tap on **The High Brow** just between your
eyebrows and while stomping your feet
say out aloud:"

I still feel a bit angry!

"Tap on **The Sigh Brow** to the side of your eye and
through gritted teeth say out aloud:"

Still a little bit angry.

"Tap on **The Low Brow** just below your eye and while screwing up your face say out aloud:"

This left-over anger.

"Tap **under your nose** and say out aloud:"

Part of me wants to stay mad.

"Tap **on your chin**, under your lip and say out aloud:"

Maybe that's why I still feel a bit angry.

"Tap **under your arms** by slapping them with your palms and say out aloud:"

It's okay. I'm still a great kid.

"Tap on **The Tarzan Thump** on your chest and say out aloud:"

*I'm a great kid and I set the rest of this anger free!
I am happy and calm and relaxed now.
I am peaceful and happy and calm.*

"How does that feel now Phoebe?"

• • •

"It's all gone now. Wow, that feels great. I don't feel angry at all anymore. Thanks TapMeister!"

• • •

"That's wonderful Phoebe. So always remember, girls and boys, to do another round or more of tapping until you feel happy and calm inside.

"Now that you have set your angry feelings free, what do you think is happening to your energy?"

• • •

"Gee I think my Chi is FREE TO FLOW now, TapMeister," confirms Angus

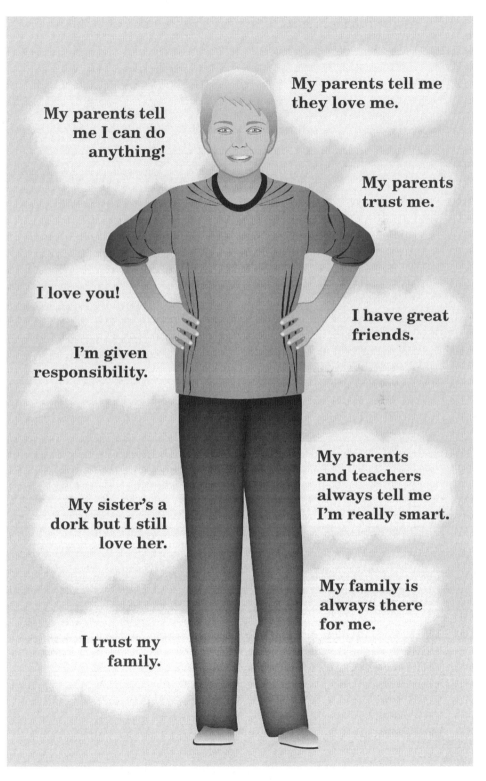

"It's weird, I feel lighter," says Dylan

"Can we do it again?" says Hannah

• • •

"Of course! I have plenty more exercises up my sleeve! Are we ready for the next Workout?"

• • •

"Yeeessss TapMeister!" call out the kids

• • •

"Our next Workout is an exercise in 'recycling' our worries. Into the elevator and up to the next floor we go!"

• • •

CHAPTER 6

The Worry Workout Room
Fourth Floor

• • •

"Our second Workout is an exercise in releasing our
worries. Do you sometimes get worried or scared,
boys and girls?"

• • •

"Yeeeesss TapMeister" the kids call out, nodding their
heads in agreement.

• • •

"What sort of things do you get scared
and worried about?"

• • •

"I worry about my mum getting sick," calls out Hannah.
"I worry about my dog getting run over," calls out Angus.

"I'm scared of being home on my own. Sometimes I hear scary noises," says Sam.

"I worry about failing my math test," calls out Phoebe.

"I worry about being teased by the older girls at school. They're very mean," says Caitlin.

"I worry about falling down in a race," calls out Antonia.

"I'm scared of going swimming again because I nearly drowned last time," calls out Evie.

"I'm scared of my neighbor's dog," calls out Josh.

"I worry about my daddy smoking cigarettes," says Sophie.

"I'm scared of going on an airplane because it might crash," says Dylan.

"I worry about making a mistake on the computer," calls out Rohan.

Second Exercise of the Day: A Big Green Recycle Bag Full of Worries

• • •

"Thank you everyone for your answers. It sounds
like we have enough worries and fears to fill up this
Big Green Recycle Bag!"

• • •

TapMeister pulls out a **Big Green Recycle Bag** and a big bunch of green tags from under a desk. He gives everyone several of the green tags apiece.

• • •

"For our next workout, I am going to get you
to dump all your worries and fears into this
Big Green Recycle Bag. This bag is specially
designed for recycling worries."

• • •

Tuning Into Your Worries

• • •

"I want you to use these **Green Worry Tags** to write
down or draw a picture of four or five of your biggest
worries right now. If you don't want anyone to know or

What if Mum gets sick?

What if Dad loses his job?

What if I fail the math test?

What if Spot gets hurt?

What if we have to move and I lose all my friends?

What if my brother gets killed?

What if I don't make the softball team?

What if really mess up the violin recital?

What if I don't get the part I want in the school play?

What if my parents get divorced?

see your worries, you can draw a symbol that shows your worry so that only you know what it means."

• • •

Getting a Worry Rating

• • •

"Now everyone, get out your **Feel-O-Meter** and with your pointer, I want you to move it to the section on your dial that shows how worried you are right now."

• • •

The kids all move their pointers to a section on their dial.

• • •

"Excellent, we all now have a **Worry** rating on our dials."

• • •

After the kids have set their **Feel-O-Meter**s, TapMeister goes around the room collecting all the tags and putting them into the **Big Green Recycle Bag**.

• • •

"We now have a **Big Green Recycle Bag** full of worries!

"Imagine if you had to carry this heavy bag full of worries around all the time. Surely you'd start to feel the weight of it! Luckily, you don't have to carry around all these worries anymore if you don't want to.

"It's time to pick up those *Magic Wands*, girls and boys, and start recycling these worries."

• • •

The Worry Workout Tapping Script

• • •

"Now while thinking about the worries you have placed in the **Big Green Recycle Bag**, begin

tapping on your **Karate Chop** and repeat this
Set Up after me."

*Even though I have this **Big Green Recycle Bag***
full of worries and fears,
I'm still a great kid and everything's okay!

Even though some of my worries are big
And some of my worries are small,
With the magic at my fingertips,
I can get rid of them all!

"Now tapping on **The Chimney Top** at the
top of your head say out aloud:"

*This **Big Green Recycle Bag** is full of ALL my worries!*

"Tap on **The High Brow** just between your
eyebrows and say out aloud:"

*Enough worries to fill up a **Big Green Recycle Bag**.*

"Tap on **The Sigh Brow** to the side of your eye
and say out aloud:"

*This **Big Green Recycle Bag** is full of all my worries.*

"Tap on **The Low Brow** just below your eye and
say out aloud:"

So many worries in my head!

"Tap **under your nose** and say out aloud:"

While some of my worries are BIG and
some of my worries are SMALL,

"Tap **on your chin**, under your lip and
say out aloud:"

Everything's okay!

"Tap **under your arms** by slapping them with your palms and say out aloud:"

Because I can get rid of them all!

"Tap on **The Tarzan Thump** on your chest and say out aloud:"

Big Green Recycle Bag *full of worries,*
It's time to throw you away.
I don't need you anymore,
Not for one more single day.
Thank you for being with me all this time,
But now the time has come to say goodbye.

"Now, take a long deep breath in and out, filling up your belly, until you see it expand! Well done everyone! That was quite a worry workout, huh?"

• • •

The Post Tapping Worry Rating

• • •

"Now back to our **Feel-O-Meter** so we can check the temperature of our feelings again. What I want you to do is think again about what was worrying you before we started tapping and then, with your pointer, I want you to move it the section on your dial that shows how worried you are about this right now."

• • •

All the kids adjust their dials. It seems everyone's worry went all the way down!

"I feel really CALM now, TapMeister," calls out Sam.

"I can't remember what I was worried about anymore," calls out Angus, looking rather puzzled.

"It's gone away," calls out Rohan, with a beaming smile.

"Can we put our worries into the **Big Green Recycle Bag** anytime we want TapMeister?" asks Jemima.

Mum takes good care of herself so she'll be fine.

Dad really knows a lot so he can always find a job.

I've studied hard for the math test. I'll do well.

Spot is safe in the yard.

My brother will come home soon.

Even if we move I can always make new friends.

I'm very athletic, so I'll make the softball team.

I've rehearsed my violin piece loads so I will do well.

If I don't get the part I want in the school play, I'll try again next year.

My parents really love each other.

• • •

"Of course," replies TapMeister, "That's a wonderful idea! Anytime you feel your worries building up inside you again, just pull out this **Big Green Recycle Bag** and write or draw all your worries on the green worry tags. Dump the tags in the bag and repeat the *Worry Workout Tapping Script*! That's sure to chew up those worries and turn them into peace and calm instead.

"Just make sure to empty your recycle bag in the recycle bin once you've finished tapping!

"I have another exercise up my sleeve. Does anyone want to know what it is?"

• • •

"Yes pleeeeease, TapMeister" call out the kids, eager to find out what the next game is about.

• • •

"Into the elevator and up to the next floor we go."

• • •

CHAPTER 7

The Sadness Workout Room
Fifth Floor

• • •

"Our third 'Workout' is an exercise
in releasing sadness."

• • •

Third Exercise of The Day: The Sadness Workout

• • •

"Do you sometimes feel hurt or sad,
girls and boys?"

• • •

"Yeeeesss TapMeister" the kids call out, nodding their
heads in agreement.

• • •

"What sort of things make you feel sad or hurt?"

• • •

"I get sad when my mum picks me up late," says Hannah.

"I feel sad when my mum and dad are fighting," says Angus.

"I feel sad when I get a bad grade in math," calls out Phoebe.

"I get sad when I don't get picked for the team," calls out Jemima.

"I get sad when people call me names," calls out Sophie.

"I feel sad when my sister won't play with me," says Agatha.

"I get sad when I feel left out," calls out Dylan.

"I feel sad when I get into trouble for something I didn't do," calls out Angus.

"I get sad when my mum says I can't use the computer," calls out Rohan.

• • •

"Being sad is no fun is it?"

• • •

"Noooo way! I hate feeling sad, I'd rather feel happy, TapMeister," replies Jemima.

"Do you have an exercise to help us work the sadness out of our energy systems?" asks Sophie.

• • •

"Why of course!"

• • •

Tuning Into Something Sad

• • •

"Let's begin by 'tuning into' something that you're feeling sad about at the moment. If nothing is making you sad at the moment, then think of something in the past that made you sad."

• • •

"I know what we do next, TapMeister," calls out Rohan. "We rate the sadness on our **Feel-O-Meter**, don't we?"

• • •

"Excellent Rohan, I think you've got the hang of this."

• • •

Kids are always making fun of me.

My best friend moved away.

My mother said she wished she'd never had me.

My grandpa died last month.

My big brother never lets me hang out with him.

I got a bad grade in social studies.

I hate my stutter.

My teacher said I'm stupid, but I'm really not. I'm dyslexic. Why won't anyone believe me?

I never get picked for any school team.

So with that said, everyone turns to their **Feel-O-Meter**s.

• • •

"Now, with your pointer, I want you to move it to
the section on your dial that shows how sad you are
right now when you think about your situation."

• • •

The kids all move their pointers to a section on their dial.

• • •

"Excellent, we all now have a sadness rating on
our dials. Remember that, when you tune into and
think about a situation that makes you sad, your
energy automatically gets disrupted. Now that we
have called up a disruption by thinking about our
sadness, let's blast it free with EFT!

"It's time to pick up those *Magic Wands*, boys and
girls, and start setting that sadness FREE!"

• • •

The Sadness Workout Tapping Script

• • •

"Tapping on your **Karate Chop**
repeat this *Set Up* after me:"

Even though I feel real sad,
And this sadness makes me feel real bad,
I'm still a great kid and I set this sadness free!

Even though I have this sadness deep inside,
And it hurts so much I want to run and hide,
I'm still a great kid and I set this sadness free!

Even though I carry this sadness in my heart.
And it makes me want to cry,
I'm still a great kid and I set this sadness free!

"Now tapping on **The Chimney Top** at the top of your head say out aloud:"

I feel real sad!

"Tap on **The High Brow** at the beginning of your brow and say out aloud:"

This sadness makes me feel read bad.

"Tap on **The Sigh Brow** to the side of your eye and say out aloud:"

I feel sad, so sad that it makes me feel bad.

"Tap on The **Low Brow** just below your eye and say out aloud:"

All this sadness I hold inside!

"Tap on the **under your nose** and say out aloud:"

It hurts so much I want to run and hide!

"Tap **on your chin** and say out aloud:"

I carry this sadness in my heart.

"Tap **under your arms** by slapping them with your palms and say out aloud:"

It hurts so much I want to cry.

"Tap on The **Tarzan Thump** on your chest and say out aloud:"

All this sadness inside of me,
Now is the time to set it free!

"Well done everyone! Now, take a long, deep breath in and out, filling up your belly until you see it expand!"

• • •

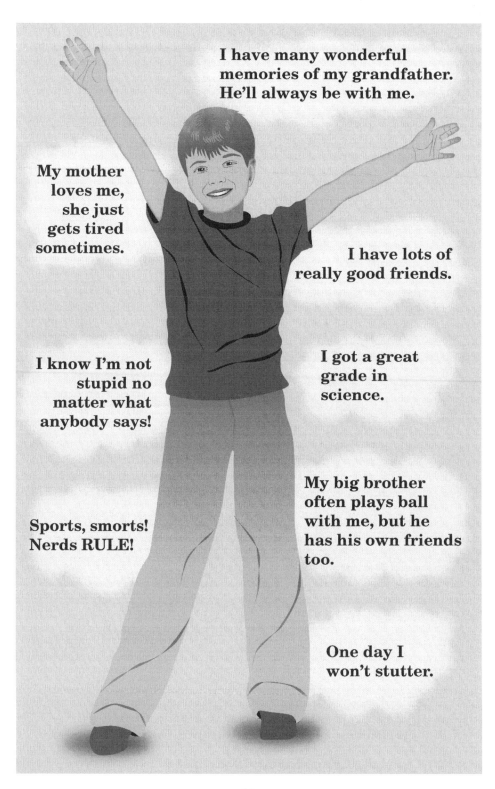

I have many wonderful memories of my grandfather. He'll always be with me.

My mother loves me, she just gets tired sometimes.

I have lots of really good friends.

I know I'm not stupid no matter what anybody says!

I got a great grade in science.

My big brother often plays ball with me, but he has his own friends too.

Sports, smorts! Nerds RULE!

One day I won't stutter.

The Post Tapping Sadness Rating

• • •

"Let's check in to see how that sadness is doing.
Using your **Feel-O-Meter**, *you* can check the
temperature of your feelings again.

"What I want you to do is think again about what
was making you feel sad before we started tapping
and then with your pointer, I want you to move it
to the section on your dial that shows how sad
you feel now."

• • •

All the kids adjust their dials. It seems everyone's sadness
went all the way down!

"I feel much happier now!" calls out Angus.

"That worked really quickly, I'm not sad about it anymore!"
calls out Jemima.

"This tapping stuff is soooo cool!" calls out Sam.

"Yeah, I don't have to feel sad if I don't want to," calls out
Phoebe. "Now I know why they're called *Magic Happy Buttons*!"

"Gee, my Chi must be flowing free now!" calls out Rohan.

"When I have other things that make me sad, I will tap on all
those too!" calls out Caitlin.

• • •

"Yes, remember you can tap anytime you feel sad.
Just 'tune in' to what is making you feel sad and
repeat the *Sadness Workout Tapping Script*.

"Well I think we might wrap up the 'Workouts' for
today! Now that you know how to work out your
anger, fears, worries, sadness and hurt, let's really
have some fun!

"I'm going to teach you how to become your very
own **Esteem Generator**. More on that when we
move up to the next floor! Into the elevator now."

• • •

CHAPTER 8

The Esteem Generator Room
Sixth Floor

**Fourth Lesson of The Day: How To Become
Your Own Esteem Generator**

"What is an Esteem Generator?" asks Josh with a puzzled look on his face.

• • •

"Well, does anyone know what 'Self Esteem' is?"

• • •

"I think it's when you feel good about yourself," calls out Rohan.

• • •

"Yes that's a very good explanation!"

• • •

• • •

"When you feel good about yourself, you feel happy
and you like yourself for who you are. That's called
having **a high self-esteem.**

"When you feel bad about yourself, you usually feel
unhappy and you don't like yourself. That's called
having **a low self-esteem.**

"When you feel good about yourself, what do you
think is happening to the energy in your body?"

• • •

"It's flowing freely!" calls out Josh.

• • •

"Indeed it is! When you feel bad about yourself,
what do you think is happening to the energy in
your body?"

• • •

"It's blocked somewhere and can't flow properly!" calls out
Angus.

• • •

"Right again! When your energy is blocked it
DROPS down low, just like an engine running low
on fuel energy.

"But when your energy is flowing freely, it goes
back UP, just like a full tank of petrol.

"The thing is, there are some things that can make
your self-esteem go UP HIGH and some things that
can make your self-esteem go LOW DOWN.

"Now let's see if we can FEEL the difference
between high and low self-esteem.

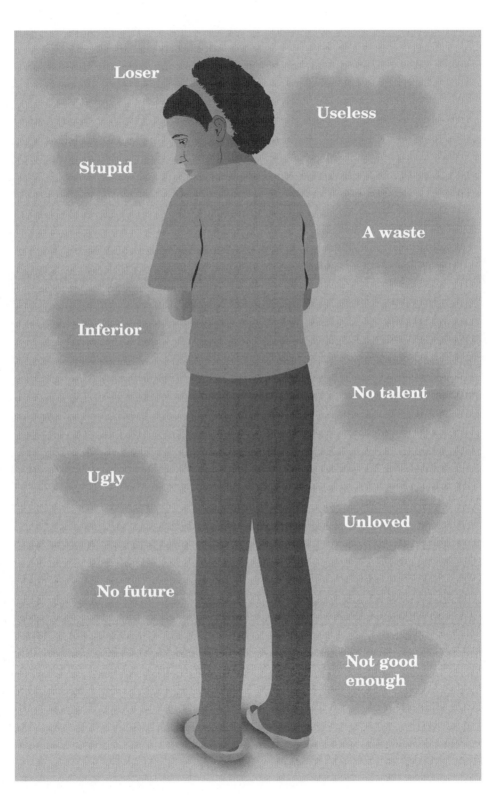

"First I want you to think of someone who has called you a name such as lazy, selfish, untidy, a nuisance, a loser, or a bragger. Maybe they've told you you're not smart enough or messy or too slow.

"What does it feel like when you imagine them calling you those names?"
• • •

"It makes me feel like I'm not good enough," says Jemima.
"It makes me feel like I'm a bad kid," calls out Hannah.
"It makes me feel like they don't love me because I'm a bad kid," calls out Dylan.
"It makes me feel weak and flat," calls out Oliver.
"It makes me feel useless," says Rohan.
"It makes me believe what they say is true; I must be a nuisance," calls out Sophie.

• • •

"Next I want you to think of someone who has told you that you are a great kid or a lovely brother, that you can win the race or you're a good person, or that you're good at something? What does it feel like when you imagine them telling you these things?"
• • •

"I feel like I'm good at something," calls out Phoebe.
"I feel good about myself," exclaims Sophie.
"I like myself more," calls out Josh.
"I feel like I'm a good kid," calls out Rohan.
"I feel like they love me," says Hannah.

• • •

"The trick here is, girls and boys, if you want HIGH self-esteem all you have to do is tap on and ERASE all the words, names and things people say to you that make you feel bad about yourself.

"After you have done that you can then choose to REPLACE these words with your very own words

that make you feel good about yourself instead.
Now isn't that a clever idea?"

• • •

The Esteem Generator Tapping Script

• • •

"Begin by thinking about some of the names people
call you—the names that makes your esteem go
down and your energy drop. Then, tapping on the
Karate Chop, repeat this *Set Up* after me:"

Even though people call me names sometimes,
Like lazy and naughty, or selfish and unkind.
I can still feel good about myself,
'Cuz I'm a great kid and one of a kind!

Even though people call me names sometimes,
Like messy and slow, or always behind.
I can still feel good about myself,
'Cuz I'm a great kid and one of a kind!

"Now while thinking about these names, tap on **The
Chimney Top** at the top of your head and say out aloud:"

These names!

"Tap on **The High Brow** at the beginning of your
brow and say out aloud:"

Make me feel like I'm not good enough.

"Tap on **The Sigh Brow** to the side of your eye and
say out aloud:"

They make me feel like I'm a bad kid.

"Tap on **The Low Brow** just below your eye and
say out aloud:"

I feel like people don't love me because I'm a bad kid.

"Tap **under your nose** and say out aloud:"

They make me feel useless.

"Tap **on your chin** and say out aloud:"

They make me feel weak and flat.

"Tap **under your arms** by slapping them with your palms and say out aloud:"

They make me believe what they say is true.

"Tap on The **Tarzan Thump** on your chest and say out aloud:"

But I can ERASE all of these names
and REPLACE them with words like:
I am Good Enough,
I like myself,
I'm a good kid,
Others love me as I am,
I'm one of a kind.

"Now, take a long deep breath in and out, filling up your belly until you see it expand! So that's the way you generate your own esteem! You are now officially your very own *Esteem Generator*."

• • •

"Wow! I'm going to generate my own esteem every day from now on, TapMeister, so that I can feel good about myself and make my self-esteem go up higher and higher," calls out Hannah.

• • •

"That's a wonderful idea Hannah!

"Okay, now join with me in doing the *Esteem Generator Rap*! It will help you to remember how to generate your own esteem."

• • •

Winner

Going Places

Smart

Important

Great

Lots of talent

Pretty

Loved

Great
future

Intelligent

The Esteem Generator Rap!

To help my esteem soar higher and higher,
I tap on my Magic Happy Buttons
To make me feel better.
So when I feel down about what someone has said,
I just turn on my Esteem Generator
And find better words to fill up my head.

I focus on what I CAN do, rather than not.
I start to remember, all the things I am good at.
I am a great kid.
I do the best I can.
I am loving and caring.
I know I am.
I am beautiful and strong,
And I love who I am.
I am peaceful and calm.
That's who I really am.

• • •

"Now, take a long deep breath in and out, filling up your belly until you see it expand! Tap along to *The Esteem Generator Rap* every day and keep your self-esteem flying high!

"Well, we have certainly covered a lot today. I'm most impressed with everyone's participation. I can hardly wait to hand out your official **Tapping Certificates** that say you've taken part in the **Palace Of Possibilities Tapping For Kids Playshop**.

"But before that, let's head up to the **Practice Room** and learn some interesting ways you can use EFT when you go home.

"Into the elevator and up to the practice room we go!"

• • •

CHAPTER 9

The Practice Room
Seventh Floor

**Fifth Lesson of the Day: The Magic Formula
for Feeling Better**

• • •

Here is a step-by-step guide to help you remember
how to do EFT on your own. Just follow the magic
formula anytime you want to feel better.

• • •

Step 1: Pick a problem, such as feeling left out at school.

Step 2: "Tune in" to the problem by thinking about it or
playing a movie of it in your mind.

Step 3: Rate the emotion using your **Feel-O-Meter**.

Step 4: Say a *Set Up* sentence such as, "Even though (I
have this problem), I'm still a great kid." Say this three times
while you tap on your karate chop.

Step 5: While thinking about your problem, tap on your *Magic Happy Buttons* starting from **The Chimney Top** all the way down to **The Tarzan Thump**.

Step 6: Rate the emotion again using your **Feel-O-Meter**.

Step 7: If your rating has gone all the way down that means you are feeling a whole lot better. If your rating has not gone all the way down, then start again and keep tapping until your rating goes all the way down.

Sixth Lesson of the Day: Problems Are Like Puzzles

• • •

"In this practice lesson you will learn that problems
are like puzzles and another important trick of
the tapping trade is to tap on all the pieces of the
puzzle to make sure the job is really done!

"When you think about your problems as puzzles,
you can see that there are different pieces joined
together to make up the whole problem and all the
bad feelings that go with it.

"Say you are being teased by someone at school.
One part of the problem may be that you are really
scared of bumping into them. The first step then is
to tap on this piece of the puzzle by tuning into this
part of the problem.

"Then when this part no longer bothers you, pick
another piece of the puzzle. You do this until you
have tapped on every piece of the puzzle until all
the bad feelings are gone."

• • •

Seventh Lesson of the Day: Practice Tapping Everyday
Try it on Everything!

• • •

"Now boys and girls, in this next practice lesson
you will learn that the real magic happens when

you start to practice tapping every day. The trick is to try it on everything! If something bothers you, then TAP on it! You'll be glad you did!

"Okay now, join me in doing the *Everyday Tap Rap*! It will help you to remember to tap everyday. While you are repeating the *Everyday Tap Rap*, remember to tap on your *Magic Happy Buttons*."

The Everyday Tap Rap!

This tapping game is such a breeze!
Now I've mastered the art, I can do it with ease!

The more I tap, the better I feel.
I can do it on my own NOW. How unreal!

It's easy to remember the best time to tap.
I do it any time I get into a flap!

I tap when I'm sad, upset or mad,
When things go wrong and I wish they never had.

The trick to remember is to tune into my problems,
Then pick up my wands and tap on my happy buttons.

I carry my wands wherever I go,
So I can tap on my happy buttons whenever I feel low

Instead of sulking, screaming and yelling,
I can now use my inner powers, to change how I'm feeling!

That's much more fun than feeling stuck.
I can do something about it NOW. Just my luck!

I can tap on my own, or with Mum or Dad,
Or with any adult, who knows the tapping trade.

I can tap anytime, in the morning or night,
In the school yard or at home,
Yes I think I just might!

• • •

"Now, take a long deep breath in and out, filling up
your belly until you see it expand!"

• • •

"That was sooo much fun, TapMeister, I am going to remember to tap every day from now on!" calls out Oliver.

• • •

"That's the trick!"

• • •

"I will try it on everything!" says Angus.

"I will try it when I feel sick," says Rohan.

"I will try it the very next time I have to go into hospital," says Oliver.

"I will try it when I get confused," says Jemima.

"I will try it when my brother teases me," says Caitlin.

"I will try it on my fear of airplanes," says Dylan.

"Oh, then I will try it on my fear of getting in the pool," says Phoebe.

"I will try it before I have a test and tap to get rid of all those worry butterflies in my stomach," says Josh.

Bed-Time Tapping

• • •

"Here's another important tip to remember kids.
Tap every night before you go to sleep. Just 'tune
in' to anything that upset you during the day and
tap on your happy buttons until you feel peaceful
and calm and sleepy. You get a great night's sleep
that way and you wake up feeling happier and more
energized."

• • •

"Thanks for the tip, TapMeister. I'm going to tap at night when I go to bed. I might take my teddy with me for comfort," says Sophie.

• • •

"You know that you can also tap on your teddy if
you want too. Teddies have *Magic Happy Buttons*
too. Just think about your problem and tap on your
teddy's buttons. It works just the same. There's
even a toy called the 'Tappy Bear' that you can use"

• • •

Teaching Others To Tap

"Can I teach other kids and adults to tap?" asks Hannah.

• • •

"Yes most certainly. Now that you've mastered the
art of tapping, you can show it to anyone who wants
to try it."

• • •

"Hmmmm" Phoebe says "I saw a girl in the younger grades
crying by herself the other day and I was wondering what I could
do to help. Maybe next time I see someone upset I can go up to
them and show them how to tap on their *Magic Happy Buttons*?"

• • •

"That would be a lovely idea. I am sure you would
do a great job too!"

• • •

"My dad gets angry a lot. Maybe I can show him how tapping
helps me feel calm and then maybe he'll try it," says Dylan.

Tapping Circles & Tapping Buddies

• • •

"Something else you could do if you wanted to, is to
find a **Tapping Buddy** or form a **Tapping Circle**
with family or a group of friends."

• • •

"Hey, that sounds like fun how do we do that?" asks Rohan.

• • •

"Having a **Tapping Buddy** means tapping with a
friend or any another kid or a brother or sister or

59

any other family member. You both tap together on something that is bothering each one of you. If you have a Tapping Buddy, you can remind and encourage each other to tap.

"Forming a **Tapping Circle** means having two or more people get together and tapping on the same sort of problem.

"So let's say you are worried and scared about all the horrible things that are happening in the world and you know other kids at school who are feeling the same. You could all get together at morning playtime or at lunch and sit in a circle in the playground, tapping on all your worries and fears. You could put all your worries and fears into the **Big Green Recycle Bag** and use the *Worry Workout Tapping Script*."

• • •

"What a fantastic idea, TapMeister!" says Dylan. "My friend Nathan and I don't like going to camp. Maybe we can start a **Tapping Circle** for kids who worry about going away to camp."

• • •

"Yes, that's the idea. You can choose any topic you want to tap on. The possibilities are endless!

"If anyone is interested in starting a **Tapping Circle** or having a **Tapping Buddy**, let me know. I have a **Starter Pack** full of all the information you need to help you set it up and keep it going."

• • •

Sharing You Tapping Stories

You can write in to the **Palace of Possibilities** at any time if you have a great story you would like to share about how tapping has helped you. Just write a letter to the TapMeister and he will publish it in his free *Kid's Tapping Newsletter* so that other kids and their parents and teachers can learn from your experience. Maybe you can report on what's happening in your **Tapping Circle**. You can also send in any questions you have about tapping and the TapMeister will post a reply via the newsletter. You or your parents and teachers can sign up for this newsletter at http://www.tappingforkids.com.

• • •

"Well now kids, the time has come to wrap up
this **Playshop**! Our final stop is the **Graduation
Room** on the top floor where everyone is presented
with a certificate.

"Into the elevator and up to the top floor!
Great views from up there!"

• • •

CHAPTER 10

The Graduation Room
Eighth Floor

The Graduation Ceremony

Excited to be graduating, the kids settle into the **Graduation Room** which is decked out with a small stage and podium. One by one, the TapMeister calls everyone up to the stage where they are presented with a **Palace of Possibilities Certificate** that states:

This is to certify that

_____

Name

Has Mastered the Art of Tapping at
The EFT Palace of Possibilities

The TapMeister

· · ·

"Congratulations! Remember to smile as you look
at the camera. Say 'eeeease!'"

· · ·

The TapMeister poses with each of the Graduates who are all proud to hold up their certificates for the camera.

A Graduation Surprise!

Kid's Tapping Survival Pack

· · ·

"As **Palace Graduates** of the **Kid's Tapping
Playshop** each one of you will also receive a **Kid's
Tapping Survival Pack** packed full of resources
and goodies to support your newly acquired
tapping skills."

· · ·

"Oh wow, what's in it TapMeister?"

· · ·

"Each **Kid's Tapping Survival Pack** contains the
following:

An Official Palace of Possibilities Tapping Poster

"This poster has a picture of where all your happy
buttons are, along with the words of the *Happy
Button Rap* and the *Magic Formula for Feeling
Better* on the back."

· · ·

Palace Of Possibilities Kid's Tapping Audio CD

· · ·

"You also take away a *Kid's Tapping CD* with the
audio recordings of all the *Tapping Scripts and
Rhymes* we have used today, including:

Finger Tapping Fun!
I Am a Ball of Energy
The Anger Workout Tapping Script
The Worry Workout Tapping Script
The Sadness Workout Tapping Script
The Esteem Generator Tapping Script
The Esteem Generator Rap!
The Everyday Tap Rap!

How To Use the Kid's Tapping CD

"Use the CD as often as you like to tap along to any of the tapping scripts. Simply 'tune in' to your problem, listen and tap.

"Here's an example. Say you are worried about a test or presentation that is coming up at school and you want to settle your nerves. You could play the *Worry Workout Tapping Script* track on your CD, either before school or in the car on the way to school, and tap along while you 'tune into' your worries. This will help settle your nerves and if after the track is over you still feel some nerves, just keep tapping on your *Magic Happy Buttons* until you feel better. This way you will feel more calm, relaxed and confident going into the test or presentation.

"Here's another example. Say you are very sad and upset with your mum because she said you couldn't have a birthday party with all your friends this year. You could play the *Sadness Workout Tapping Script* track on your audio CD while you 'tune into' your sadness and tap along. If after the track is over, you still feel sad, keep tapping until you feel better. This way you will be able to focus on enjoying your birthday, no matter what you do.

"Another great idea is to play the *Esteem Generator Rap* before you go to bed, especially if you've had a tough day and need a boost of confidence."

• • •

Kid's Tapping Circles & Tapping Buddy Start Up Guide

• • •

"This start-up guide has all the information you need to set up a tapping circle or tapping buddy system."

• • •

Kid's Tapping Tips Page

• • •

"This page gives you summary of the tips, tricks and tools of the tapping trade. Keep it in your bag or hang it up in your room as a handy reminder. Read it often to help you get the most out of tapping."

• • •

Palace of Possibilities Playshop Flyers—Join The Tapping Trend

• • •

"Your Pack also contains the official **Palace Flyer** that you can hand out to other kids you know who may like to come along to a **Playshop** to learn the art of tapping for themselves."

• • •

"Wow! So many goodies to take away. That's a big help, Tap-Meister, thank you!" calls out Sophie.

"I can't wait to play my CD," says Dylan.

"I think my cousin Jessica will love this **Playshop**. I'm going to give her a flyer!" calls out Hannah.

"I'm going to keep my *Tapping Tips Page* in my locker," says Oliver.

• • •

"It sounds like you are all going to make very good use of your *Tapping Survival Packs*!

"Guess what? It's now time for the After Graduation Party!"

• • •

"Yeeeeay!"

After Graduation Party!

• • •

"Even though this **Playshop** has come to an end, your new tapping adventures have only just begun! Happy tapping!

"It's now time to sing, dance, play and have fun!

"Let's end the day with the official **Palace Theme Song**, *Finger Tapping Fun*, shall we?

"You can clap or tap to this one!"

• • •

Finger Tapping Fun!

Rap-a-tap tapping
With my fingers,
Rap-a-tap tapping
On my face,
Rap-a-tap tapping
Is energizing!
And helps me find
My happy place!

Rap-a-tap tapping
With my fingers,
Rap-a-tap tapping
On my face,
Rap-a-tap tapping
Calms me down
And helps me find
My peaceful space!

The TapMeister puts on some energetic dance music to set the **After Graduation Party** mood. Feeling happy and free, the kids dance, laugh and sing the afternoon away!

When all the celebrations are over, the TapMeister once again swings open the door of the **Palace of Possibilities**. With a warm, glowing smile, he sends the kids home, knowing that the **Palace** and its magic will live long in their hearts and minds!

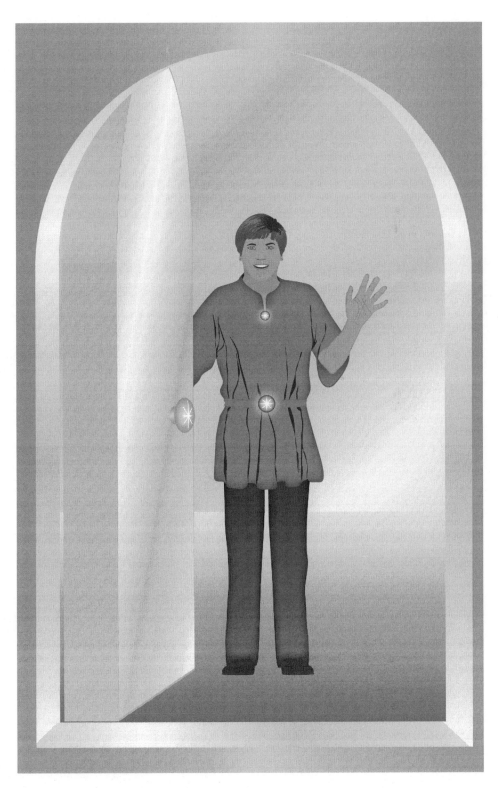

The TapMeister's Glossary of Terms

Activate: to start up or switch on.

Certificate: a piece of paper that says you have completed a course

Chi: the Chinese word for energy flow

Circuits: a closed path where energy travels

Courses: runs through

Disruption (energy): a break in the flow of energy

EFT: stands for Emotional Freedom Technique

Emotions: a strong feeling or response such as anger, sadness, joy, worry that also has a physical part to it such as trembling, crying, laughing, heart racing, sweaty palms.

Energy: to power something up

Feel-o-Meter: a dial used to measure the intensity of feelings

Flow: to move steadily and easily like a stream

Generator: to create something

Happy Buttons: the name given to EFT tapping points

Internal: located on the inside

Invisible: cant' be seen

Magic Wands: the name given for fingertips used in tapping

Master: to become very good at something

Meister: the German word for Master

Meridians: energy pathways in the body

Movement: a group of people doing something to achieve a common goal; e.g., peace movement

Multi-level: a building with many floors

Playshop: a workshop for kids, involves learning through games and fun activities

Possibilities: where anything can happen.

Problem: something that is difficult to understand or deal with

Recycle: to change something into something else. To use it for something else.

Self-esteem: to have a high opinion of yourself

Set up: a description of the problem you want to tap on. It is said while tapping on the karate chop (side of the hand).

Skill: the ability to do a task well

Tapping: using fingertips to lightly strike points on the body

Trade: a craft or skill

Trend: the latest style or thing

Tuning in: thinking about a problem

The TapMeister's Recommended Resources and Links

EFT for Kids

Tapping For Kids Official Website:
www.tappingforkids.com

Eddie Brady: Creator of Feel-o-Meter
www.breakingfree.biz

Till Shilling: Creator of Tappy Bear
www.tappybear.com

EFT Kids Forum
www.eft4kids.org

School Made Much Easier with EFT
www.schoolmademucheasier.com

EFT For Adults

Adventures In EFT—Dr Silvia Hartmann
www.dragonrising.com

Art & Science of Emotional Freedom—Ananga Sivyer
wwww.dragonrising.com

Life Without Panic Attacks—Nicola Quinn
www.dragonrising.com

EFT World Centre
www.emofree.com

EFT For Professionals

Advanced Patterns of EFT—Dr Silvia Hartmann
www.dragonrising.com

Practitioner Of Meridian Energy Therapies—Distance
Learning Course
www.Sidereus.org

EFT Training Program
www.emofree.com

About The Author

Angie Muccillo is a Complimentary Health Practitioner from Melbourne Australia, who is trained in Advanced EFT, Remedial Massage and Reiki Level II. Angie is enthusiastic and passionate about sharing and teaching others, including children, how to use Energy Therapies for emotional healing, personal development and to gain powerful relief from the physical and emotional stresses of everyday life.

Angie graduated from Monash University Gippsland in 1988 with a Bachelor of Arts Degree in Sociology and Psychology. She spent the following 15 years working in the disability field where she gained extensive experience in developing and implementing specialized education and training programs, assisting people with disabilities to develop life skills and access mainstream services.

Angie has been practicing EFT on a personal level and training in its methods since 2002.

Angie currently conducts workshops in EFT and offers individual consultations for pain management, stress management, anxiety, self esteem, quit smoking, trauma, fears and phobias, children, parenting and pregnancy issues.

Tapping For Kids is Angie's first book and is inspired by a strong desire to put EFT into the hands of young people as a tool to help them overcome their fears, worries and everyday traumas as well as build their self-esteem.

Contact details:
Angie Muccillo
www.tappingforkids.com
sublime@pacific.net.au
Phone: 61 417 391 055
Melbourne Victoria Australia